JAZZ PIANO QUICK STUDIES GRADES 1-5

The Associated Board of the Royal Schools of Music

Introduction

Playing unprepared in a lively, creative, musical and accurate way is at the very heart of jazz performance. All jazz musicians have their own vocabulary which they use as a basis for their playing; but they must also be able to improvise spontaneously, or 'unprepared', on a piece previously unheard. The quick study tests this ability (without meaning that you should be unprepared for the exam!), helping you to learn repertoire effectively and preparing you for the very real demands of busking through those unrehearsed situations which are so often a feature of the jazz musician's life.

Jazz is an aural tradition, and the ability to pick up new material and recreate it by ear as well as from notation is vital. Some of the most interesting repertoire cannot be written down satisfactorily, and listening and copying is often the only way to get inside the style of the music, its phrasing, its inflections and its expressive embellishments. Reading staff notation is therefore just one of several ways in which you can learn jazz repertoire; recordings, friends and teachers are other important sources, and the option of doing the quick study by ear is also available.

In order to learn and really understand the style and the repertoire of jazz from the inside, jazz musicians should regularly practise both reading music fluently and musically from the page and copying music fluently and musically directly from what they hear. The Board's syllabus will introduce you to these necessary skills, while at the same time reflecting the richness and variety of the idiom.

The Practice Tests

Grooves
The practice tests cover a wide range of musical styles within the idiom. Even at Grade 1, you will play in both swing and straight quavers, and use swing, rock and latin grooves. The tempo, indicated by a metronome mark, should also be followed.

The scale or mode and guideline pitches
You will be given the scale or mode of the test before playing and, although other pitches may be incorporated as desired, this should form the basis of your improvisation. As in the pieces, guideline pitches are given for those reading from the page, while the name of the relevant scale or mode is given and the initial pitch sounded and named for those working by ear. It is expected that you will be able to use the pitches more flexibly as you progress, working from small three- or four-note pitch groups to full scales as fluency and control develops. As a starting-point you might find it useful to try using the same pitches as those in the short head for your improvisation. Those working from notation may also like to refer to the given chord symbols from Grade 4 onwards, while those working by ear will use the sound of the bass-line as the basis of their harmonic perspective on the given part.

Key signatures
At Grades 1 and 2 the key signature of the quick study follows that of the scale given on which to improvise. At Grades 3 to 5, where the studies are longer, a sense of key or mode emerges. This is reflected in the key signature given.

By ear or from notation — work on both!

Ideally you should practise doing the quick studies both ways — by ear *and* from notation — as both are essential jazz skills. Ultimately, however, a successful performance of the quick study depends on the accurate rendition of the head and a suitable and musical improvisation, not on whether you did it by ear or notation, so put your best foot forward in the exam itself.

Extending and developing the activities of the exam

With your teacher and fellow students, extend and develop these short tests to make real music; repeat them round and round for improvisation practice and invent new starting-points of a similar sort yourselves. You could even use a two- or four-bar passage from one of the pieces you are learning as a basis for this activity. The chapter on the quick study in *Jazz Piano from Scratch* gives some helpful advice on different ways to extend this work.

The Exam

Each study consists of two sections: one which must be recreated and the other improvised. At Grades 4 and 5 a simple, repeated left-hand part is included, which continues through both sections. The phrase for recreation and your improvisation will be based on the scale indicated. This scale will be any one of those set for the grade or, for Grades 2 and above, from the preceding grades. The test may be in either swing or straight quavers, and will indicate whether it is in a swing, rock or latin groove.

If you opt to play at sight, the examiner will give you the pulse and then a short interval of up to half a minute in which to look through and, if you wish, try out any part of the test before you are required to perform it for assessment. The examiner will then count you in.

If you opt to play by ear, the examiner will state the scale being used, sound and name the starting note or notes, and indicate the pulse. The given passage will be played three times by the examiner, and there will be a short interval after the second and third playings during which you may try out what you have heard. For Grades 4 and 5, where the left hand is added, the examiner will play the bass-line as an introductory groove to the first playing (this introduction shouldn't be included in your performance). The examiner will then count you in, clearly indicating the downbeat in cases where the phrase begins after the first beat of the bar.

In both cases, credit will be given to those who observe the musical character of the given phrase as well as playing it accurately. If you are working by ear, listen not only to the pitches and rhythms but to the general mood and character, often defined by the speed, the pulse, the rhythmic style, the dynamics and the phrasing. You may find it easier to gain marks by achieving these aspects of the performance, even if the odd pitch is out of place. If you are working from the page, you should observe these same requirements carefully. The improvisation should remain broadly within the given style, though distinctive and lively improvising is also encouraged. A solid sense of pulse and a positive yet relaxed rhythmic drive are at the heart of the style. (Reference should be made to the syllabus for the criteria against which the examiner will be making an overall assessment.)

Jazz Piano: The CD (available for each grade separately) illustrates how the quick study will be taken in the exam by both by ear and from notation candidates. Each recorded test is indicated by the symbol (CD) in this book.

Summary

The skills tested in the quick study will provide the foundation for successful jazz playing in the years to come. Working carefully through this book, and exploring the various activities as recommended above and in *Jazz Piano from Scratch*, will therefore be a worthwhile investment.

Charles Beale

QUICK STUDIES   Grade 1

To play *either* at sight *or* by ear (see Introduction), at the choice of the candidate, a two-bar passage for one hand only and improvise a two-bar continuation based on the scale indicated and used for bars 1 and 2. This scale will be any one of those set for this Grade. The first two bars will be fully notated in 4/4 time and written in the treble clef within the range of a fourth. Chord symbols will also be provided.

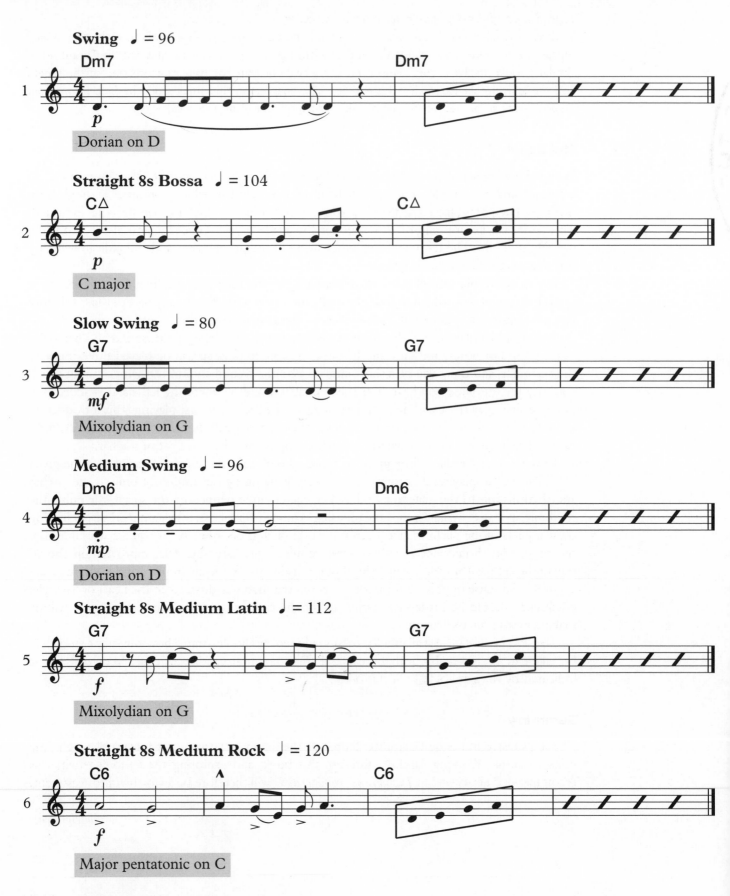

AB 2638

QUICK STUDIES   Grade 1

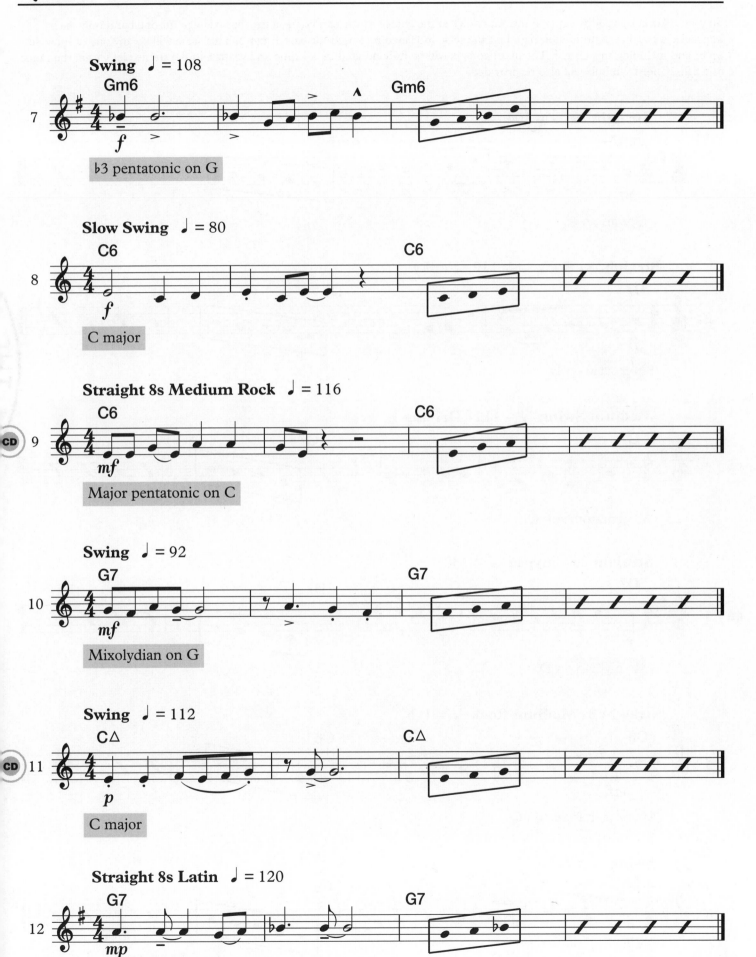

Swing ♩ = 108
Gm6   Gm6
♭3 pentatonic on G

Slow Swing ♩ = 80
C6   C6
C major

Straight 8s Medium Rock ♩ = 116
C6   C6
Major pentatonic on C

Swing ♩ = 92
G7   G7
Mixolydian on G

Swing ♩ = 112
C△   C△
C major

Straight 8s Latin ♩ = 120
G7   G7
♭3 pentatonic on G

QUICK STUDIES   Grade 2

To play *either* at sight *or* by ear (see Introduction), at the choice of the candidate, a two-bar passage for one hand only and improvise a two-bar continuation based on the scale indicated and used for bars 1 and 2. This scale will be any one of those set up to and including this Grade. The first two bars will be fully notated in 4/4 time and written in the treble clef within the range of a fifth. Chord symbols will also be provided.

QUICK STUDIES   Grade 2

QUICK STUDIES   Grade 3

To play *either* at sight *or* by ear (see Introduction), at the choice of the candidate, a four-bar passage for one hand only and improvise a four-bar continuation based on the scale indicated and used for bars 1 to 4. This scale will be any one of those set up to and including this Grade. The first four bars will be fully notated in 4/4 time and within the range of a sixth. Chord symbols will also be provided.

Straight 8s ♩ = 104

Lydian on B♭

Medium Swing ♩ = 104

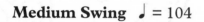

Blues scale on F

Straight 8s Rock ♩ = 104 **Driving**

Blues scale on C

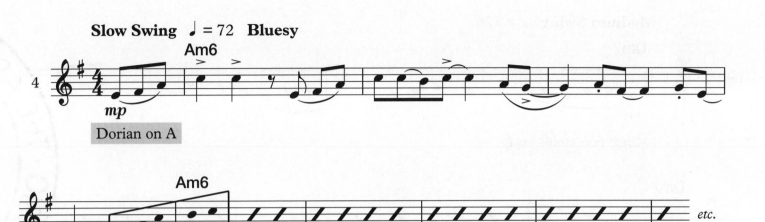

Medium Swing ♩ = 126

Minor pentatonic on D

Straight 8s Latin ♩ = 132

Lydian on B♭

Straight 8s Bossa ♩ = 108

Minor pentatonic on A

QUICK STUDIES Grade 3

Swing ♩ = 112

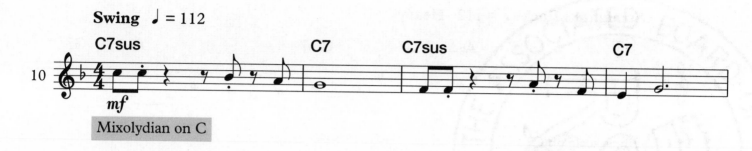

Mixolydian on C

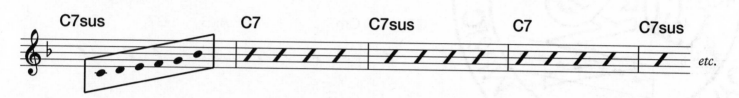

Straight 8s Rock ♩ = 96

F major

Straight 8s Latin ♩ = 96

Minor pentatonic on C

QUICK STUDIES   Grade 4

To play *either* at sight *or* by ear (see Introduction), at the choice of the candidate, a four-bar passage and improvise a four-bar continuation based on the scale indicated and used for bars 1 to 4. This scale will be any one of those set up to and including this Grade. The first four bars will be fully notated in 3 or 4 time and within the range of an octave in the right-hand part. The left-hand part will be restricted to playing a very simple bass line. Chord symbols will also be provided.

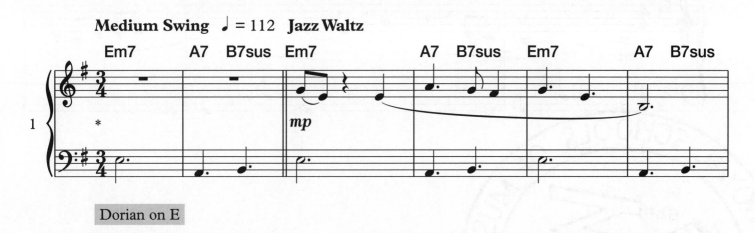

Dorian on E

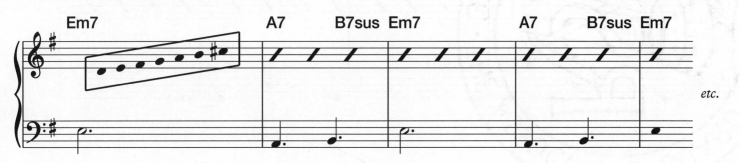

Blues scale on B♭

* Example of introductory groove for by ear candidate (see Introduction).

Straight 8s Bossa ♩ = 108

Lydian on G

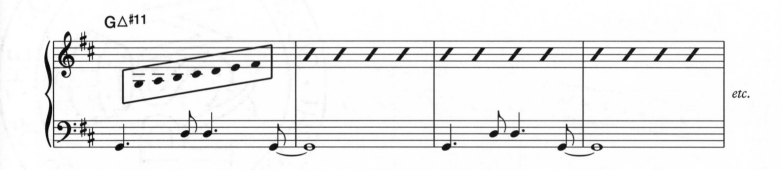

etc.

Straight 8s Rock ♩ = 96 **Heavy**

Blues scale on E

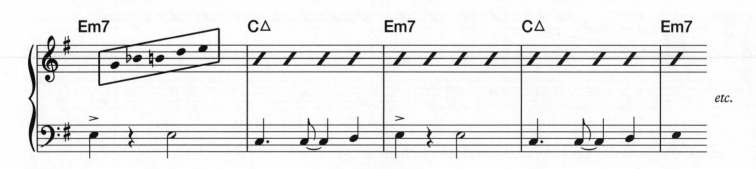

etc.

QUICK STUDIES   Grade 4

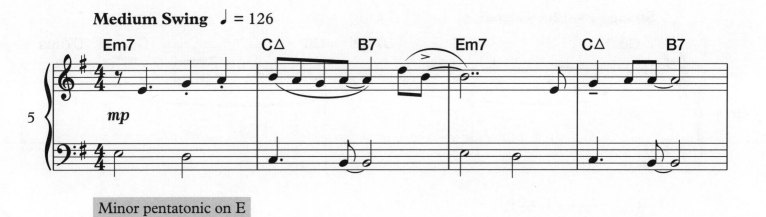

Minor pentatonic on E

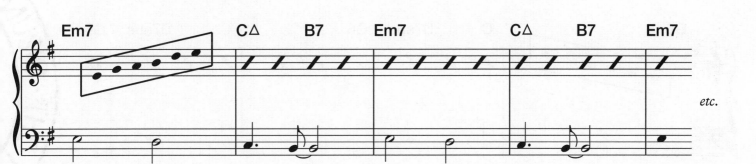

etc.

Mixolydian on A

etc.

QUICK STUDIES   Grade 4

Swing ♩ = 120 **Gospel**

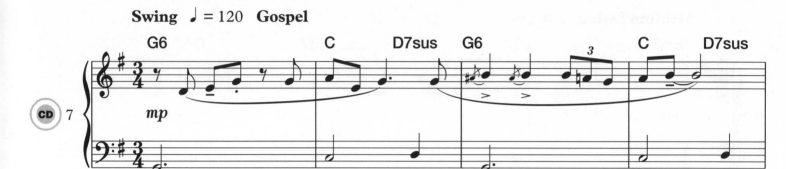

CD 7

Major pentatonic on G

etc.

Straight 8s Latin ♩ = 116

8

Lydian on E♭

etc.

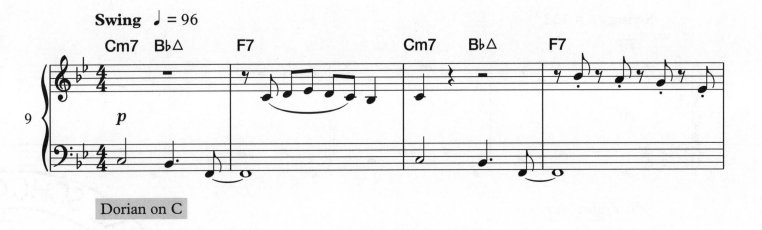

Dorian on C

etc.

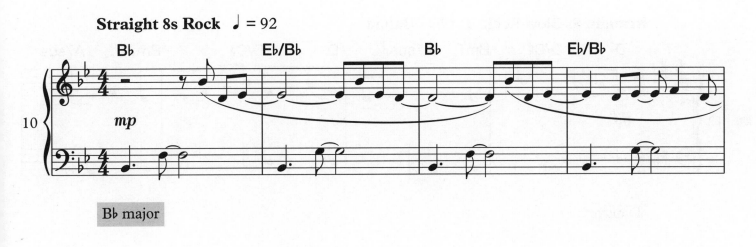

B♭ major

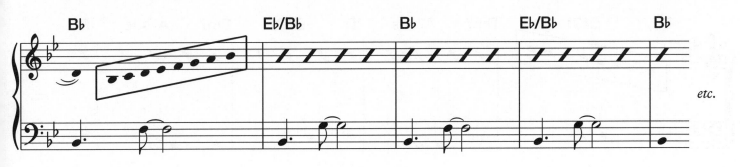

etc.

QUICK STUDIES   Grade 4

Swing ♩ = 132

Mixolydian on F

etc.

Straight 8s Slow Rock ♩ = 63 **Ballad**

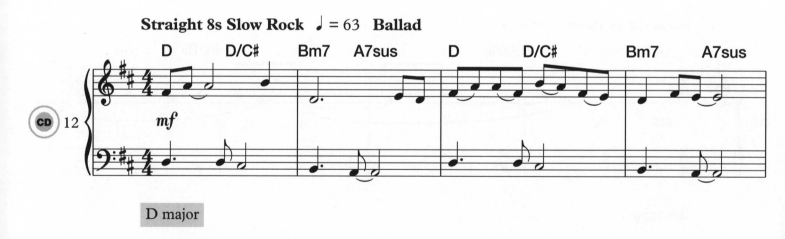

D major

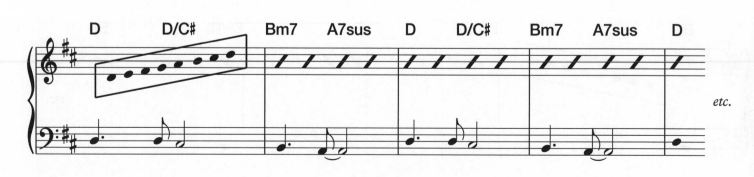

etc.

Major pentatonic on F

etc.

Major pentatonic on E♭

etc.

QUICK STUDIES   Grade 4

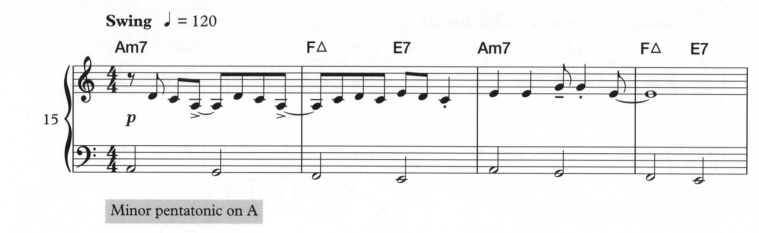

Minor pentatonic on A

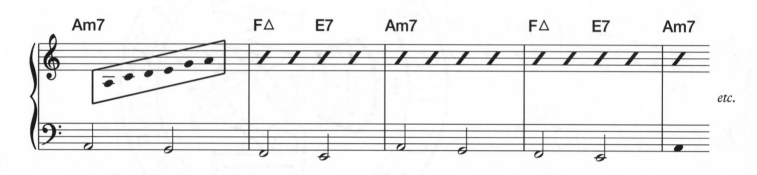

etc.

Blues scale on B♭

etc.

QUICK STUDIES Grade 5

To play *either* at sight *or* by ear (see Introduction), at the choice of the candidate, a four-bar passage and improvise a four-bar continuation based on the scale indicated and used for bars 1 to 4. This scale will be any one of those set up to and including this Grade. The first four bars will be fully notated in 3 or 4 time and within the range of a tenth in the right-hand part. The left-hand part throughout will consist of a simple bass line, while the right-hand melodic part may include two-note chords. Chord symbols will also be provided.

* Example of introductory groove for by - ear candidate (see Introduction).

AB 2638

QUICK STUDIES   Grade 5

Straight 8s Bossa ♩ = 116

3

mf

Dorian on B

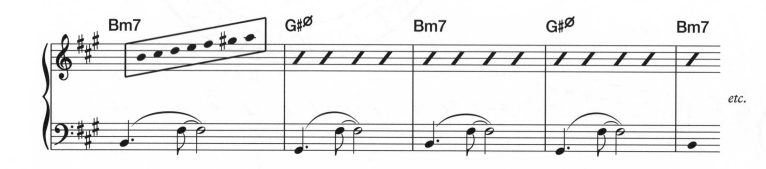

etc.

Swing ♩ = 120

CD 4

f

Blues scale on A

etc.

QUICK STUDIES Grade 5

Straight 8s Latin ♩ = 84

Lydian on C

etc.

Straight 8s Rock ♩ = 120 **Funky**

♭3 pentatonic on G

etc.

Straight 8s Medium Latin ♩ = 126

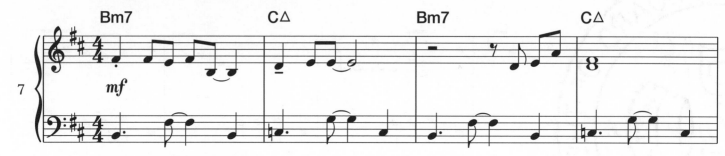

Minor pentatonic on B

etc.

Swing ♩ = 112

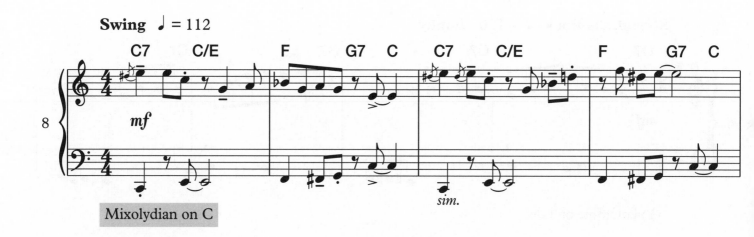

Mixolydian on C

etc.

Straight 8s Slow Rock ♩ = 92

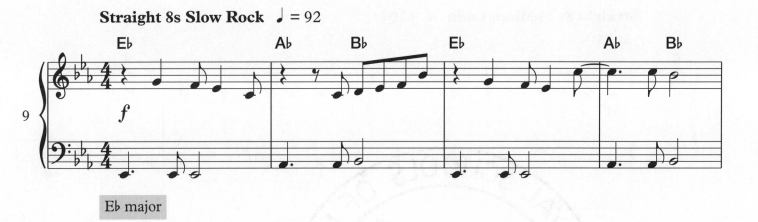

Eb major

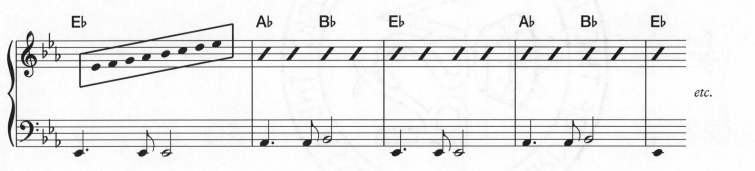

etc.

Swing ♩ = 116

Blues scale on G

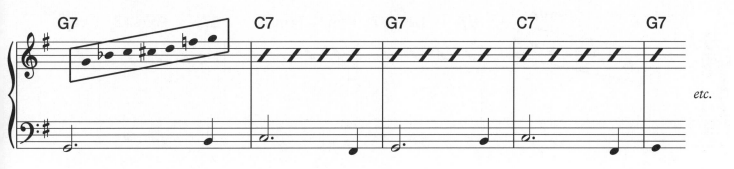

etc.

QUICK STUDIES Grade 5

Straight 8s Medium Latin ♩ = 104

Lydian on A♭

etc.

Swing ♩ = 92

Blues scale on F♯

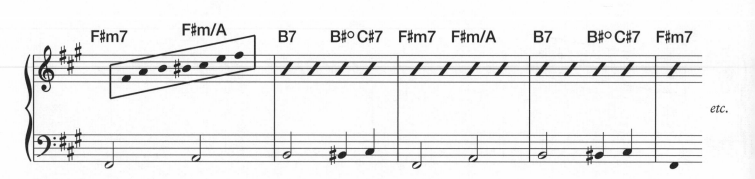

etc.

QUICK STUDIES   Grade 5

Straight 8s Slow Latin/Brazilian ♩ = 96

Dorian on F

etc.

Swing ♩ = 112   **Bright and cheerful**

Major pentatonic on B♭

etc.

28

Straight 8s Rock ♩ = 116

15

Lydian on D

etc.

Swing ♩ = 120

16

Minor pentatonic on G

etc.

QUICK STUDIES Grade 5

Straight 8s Rock ♩ = 132

Lydian on F

etc.

Swing ♩ = 126

Dorian on F

Fm6

etc.

Straight 8s Latin ♩ = 120

19

Mixolydian on B♭

etc.

Straight 8s Rock ♩ = 92 **Dig in**

20

Major pentatonic on D

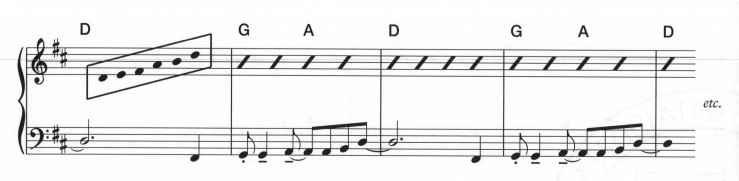

etc.

Printed in England by Caligraving Limited Thetford Norfolk